TROPICAL AN

by
E. M. NOLL

BERNARD BABANI (publishing) LTD
THE GRAMPIANS
SHEPHERDS BUSH ROAD
LONDON W6 7NF
ENGLAND

PLEASE NOTE

Although every care has been taken with the production of this book to ensure that any projects, designs, modifications and/or programs etc. contained herein, operate in a corrrect and safe manner and also that any components specified are normally available in Great Britain, the Publishers do not accept responsibility in any way for the failure, including fault in design, of any project, design, modification or program to work correctly or to cause damage to any other equipment that it may be connected to or used in conjunction with, or in respect of any other damage or injury that may be so caused, nor do the Publishers accept responsibility in any way for the failure to obtain specified components.

Notice is also given that if equipment that is still under warranty is modified in any way or used or connected with home-built equipment then that warranty may be void.

© 1984 BERNARD BABANI (publishing) LTD

First Published – August 1984

British Library Cataloguing in Publication Data
Noll, Edward M.
      25 simple tropical and M.W. band aerials.
      – (BP145)
      1. Radio-Antennas
      I. Title
      621.3841'35   TK6565.A6
      ISBN 0 85934 120 8

Printed and Bound in Great Britain by Cox & Wyman Ltd, Reading

ABOUT THE AUTHOR

Ed Noll is an established American technical author who has written many books, articles and instruction manuals as well as having lectured and taught radio communication at various universities in the U.S.A.

He has worked on the staff of a number of broadcasting stations and as a consulting engineer.

CONTENTS

Page

PERSPECTIVE

The aerials in this book are planned for operation on the medium-wave broadcast band (550—1600 kHz) and the tropical bands. The tropical bands are the 60, 75, 90 and 120 metre bands. They are referred to as tropical bands because of the predominance of broadcast signals that originate in the equatorial regions. Actually these frequencies are excellent for conveying regional and local broadcast signals. Aerials for the 49 metre band are also included. This band features a combination of regional and long-distance signals.

Your aerial is the sensor that is activated by radio signals reaching your location from all parts of the world. Modern short-wave receivers are so sensitive that built-in, indoor and very simple outdoor aerials derive adequate signals from many of the high-powered radio broadcast stations. However, there are a number of advantages in having a well-planned efficient outdoor aerial system. Such an aerial is important in receiving weak broadcast signals, particularly when you are trying to make a positive identification. If you are interested in receiving the very best signal from both strong and weak incoming signals, the aerial is important in minimizing the ill effects of fast fading, background interference and selective-fading (distortion that results from some frequencies that comprise an incoming signal fade in-and-out relative to others). For example, a solid locked-in signal is preferred by the avid music fan. A good aerial can aid in the minimization of signal-generated (QRM) and static (QRN) interference. More than one station may occupy the same frequency or a signal from an adjacent channel may be especially strong, producing objectionable interference. Often a directional aerial is helpful in emphasizing a desired signal and attenuating an undesired one. Fortunately good aerials can be erected at low cost, and for a small fractional part of the cost of your receiving equipment. This book tells the story.

A series of 25 aerials are covered. However, it is helpful if you start by reading the Perspective and the discussions about the first ten aerial types presented. Many of the principles, ideas and construction procedures covered can be used again in the planning of the aerials that follow.

You may wish to check and compare two or more aerials to find one best suited to your needs and location. To compare one aerial to another, do so directly using a switch or some other means of making a fast changeover. You can not make an accurate comparison by taking one aerial down and replacing it with another because of the rapidity of propagation changes.

Tropical and MW Bands

The official ITU bands are listed in Table 1. It should be stressed that broadcast stations cannot only be found within the frequency limits of the official bands. A host of stations operate above and below the frequency limits and, to a limited extent, on other more widely separated frequencies. A few are pirate stations and not officially allocated by their countries.

Table 1 ITU Bands

Band (metres)	Frequency (MHz)	Band (metres)	Frequency (MHz)
49	5.95 - 6.20	90	3.20 – 3.40
60	4.78 - 5.06	120	2.30 – 2.498
75	3.95 - 4.00	MW	(kHz)
		Broadcast	550 – 1600

Aerial Directivity

Many aerials, even the simpler types, have directional characteristics. Some aerials can be planned to be highly directional and can be erected to favour specific countries. In erecting a directional aerial it is important that you know the compass bearings of your particular erection site. An accurate compass is a big help. The second bit of information that you must know is the particular angles (azimuth) of the stations to be received from your site. Fortunately, most aerials that you

2

would use for broadcast listening have a wide selectivity response and orientation is not especially critical. Nevertheless you can do some favouring that can be helpful. Details will follow later on.

Some typical receive angles from the capital cities of London, England; Ottawa, Canada; Canberra, Australia; Wellington, New Zealand and Washington, D.C., U.S.A. to eleven countries are given in Table 2. Such stations can be of help in checking and comparing aerials. As mentioned previously, precise orientation for even rather highly directional aerials are not critical except for narrow-beam yagi, loop and beverage aerials. Orientation off 25° or more would be barely noticeable because of broad beam widths and strong incoming signals. Reception angles, mileage figures and a variety of data for more than 200 short-wave stations from your particular location may be obtained at low cost from Process Analysis Corp., 22nd Avenue, NW, Seattle, Washington, 98177, U.S.A.

If you plan to do a considerable amount of aerial testing a copy of the World Radio TV Handbook (WRTH) is very helpful. It can be purchased in almost every country of the world that has sales outlets for short-wave broadcast receiving equipment. Frequencies, schedules, powers and a vast amount of additional information are included.

Time Standard Stations
In addition to high-powered broadcast stations there are a variety of stations that transmit time and frequency standard signals. Some of these stations are in, or adjacent to, several short-wave broadcast bands. Table 3 is a partial listing. Many of these stations are on the air continuously and can be easily identified. They are excellent for making aerial comparisons.
A time signal is located either in-band or just off-band for each of the tropical bands.

Time Zones
Another factor in making aerial checks and matching test time with the schedule of an overseas broadcast transmission is an understanding of time zones. The International Telecommunications Union has established universal time coordinated

Table 2 Typical Azimuth Angles to Sample Locations

Azimuth Angles From

Country/Town	London	Ottawa	Canberra	Wellington	Washington D.C.
Australia, Melbourne	74	268	—	268	257
Canada, Sackville	288	—	56	63	49
New Zealand, Wellington	20	248	113	—	243
England, London	—	53	315	342	49
USA, Washington D.C.	287	175	70	68	—
Brazil, Brasilia	226	150	159	135	147
China, Beijing	45	350	335	318	349
Germany, Cologne	95	52	312	324	44
Japan, Tokyo	31	331	352	332	330
Spain, Madrid	193	68	290	225	63
South Africa, Johannesburg	154	100	230	210	103
USSR, Moscow	64	34	316	312	32

4

Table 3
Aerial-checking Standard Time and Frequency Stations

USA Fort Collins, Colorado (WWV)
2.5 MHz – 5 MHz – 10 MHz – 15 MHz – 20 MHz
(continuous)

USA Kauai, Hawaii (WWVH)
2.5 MHz – 5 MHz – 10 MHz – 15 MHz
(continuous)

CANADA Ottawa, Ontario (CHU)
3.33 MHz – 7.335 MHz – 14.67 MHz
(continuous)

AUSTRALIA Lyndhurst, Victoria (VNG)
4.5 MHz   0945–2130 UTC
7.5 MHz   2245–2230 UTC
12 MHz   2145–0930 UTC

USSR Moscow (RWM)
4.996 MHz – 9.996 MHz – 14.996 MHz

(UTC) zones based on a 24-hour clock 0000 to 2400. This is the same as the long-used Greenwich Mean Time (GMT). Broadcast stations schedules and short-wave listening newsletters and magazines use this universal time. It is your responsibility to make the necessary conversion to local time. No such conversion is required for the United Kingdom except to add on one hour during summer-time. Canada has six zones. The number of hours to be subtracted from the UTC time is given in Table 4. Similar relations exist for the United States of America with the exception that the U.S.A. has only four time zones. As an example, when it is 12 noon (12 UTC) in London, it is five hours earlier in Washington, D.C., (1200 – 0500) or 7 a.m. Time is advanced one hour for daylight time in each zone. New Zealand has only one time zone which is ahead of UTC by 12 hours. Midnight in London is noon in New Zealand. Australia has four time zones.

Table 4 Universal Time and Time Zones

CANADIAN TIME ZONES

UTC	NEWFOUNDLAND	ATLANTIC	EST	CST	MST	PST
0000M	2030	8.30 PM	8 PM	7 PM	6 PM	5 PM	4 PM
0100	2130	9.30	9	8	7	6	5
0200	2230	10.30	10	9	8	7	6
0300	2330	11.30	11	10	9	8	7
0400	0030	12.30	12 M	11	10	9	8
0500	0130	1.30 AM	1 AM	12 M	11	10	9
0600	0230	2.30	2	1 AM	12 M	11	10
0700	0330	3.30	3	2	1 AM	12 M	11
0800	0430	4.30	4	3	2	1 AM	12 M
0900	0530	5.30	5	4	3	2	1 AM
1000	0630	6.30	6	5	4	3	2
1100	0730	7.30	7	6	5	4	3
1200N	0830	8.30	8	7	6	5	4
1300	0930	9.30	9	8	7	6	5
1400	1030	10.30	10	9	8	7	6
1500	1130	11.30	11	10	9	8	7
1600	1230	12.30 PM	12 N	11	10	9	8

		1.30 PM	1 PM	12 N	11AM	10 AM	9 AM
1700	1330	1.30 PM	1 PM	12 N	11AM	10 AM	9 AM
1800	1430	2.30	2	1 PM	12 N	11	10
1900	1530	3.30	3	2	1 PM	12 N	11
2000	1630	4.30	4	3	2	1 PM	12 N
2100	1730	5.30	5	4	3	2	1 PM
2200	1830	6.30	6	5	4	3	2
2300	1930	7.30	7	6	5	4 .	3
2400	2030	8.30	8	7	6	5	4

USA TIME ZONES

UTC	EST	EST	EDT	CST	MST	PST
0000M	1900	7 PM	8 PM	6 PM	5 PM	4 PM
0100	2000	8	9	7	6	5
0200	2100	9	10	8	7	6
0300	2200	10	11	9	8	7
0400	2300	11	12 M	10	9	8
0500	2400	12 M	1 AM	11	10	9
0600	0100	1 AM	2	12 M	11	10

USA TIME ZONES (continued)

UTC	EST	EST	EDT	CST	MST	PST
0700	0200	2 AM	3 AM	1 AM	12 M	11 PM
0800	0300	3	4	2	1 AM	12 M
0900	0400	4	5	3	2	1 AM
1000	0500	5	6	4	3	2
1100	0600	6	7	5	4	3
1200N	0700	7	8	6	5	4
1300	0800	8	9	7	6	5
1400	0900	9	10	8	7	6
1500	1000	10	11	9	8	7
1600	1100	11	12 N	10	9	8
1700	1200	12 N	1 PM	11	10	9
1800	1300	1 PM	2	12 N	11	10
1900	1400	2	3	1 PM	12 N	11
2000	1500	3	4	2	1 PM	12 N
2100	1600	4	5	3	2	1 PM
2200	1700	5	6	4	3	2
2300	1800	6	7	5	4	3
2400	1900	7	8	6	5	4

AUSTRALIAN TIME ZONE

UTC	VICT	VICT	NA–SA	WA
0000M	1000	10 AM	9.30 AM	8 AM
0100	1100	11	10.30	9
0200	1200 N	12 N	11.30	10
0300	1300	1 PM	12.30 PM	11
0400	1400	2	1.30	12 N
0500	1500	3	2.30	1 PM
0600	1600	4	3.30	2
0700	1700	5	4.30	3
0800	1800	6	5.30	4
0900	1900	7	6.30	5
1000	2000	8	7.30	6
1100	2100	9	8.30	7
1200 N	2200	10	9.30	8
1300	2300	11	10.30	9
1400	2400M	12 M	11.30	10
1500	0100	1 AM	12.30 AM	11
1600	0200	2	1.30	12 M
1700	0300	3	2.30	1 AM

AUSTRALIAN TIME ZONE (continued)

UTC	VICT	VICT	NA–SA	WA
1800	0400	4 AM	3.30 AM	2 AM
1900	0500	5	4.30	3
2000	0600	6	5.30	4
2100	0700	7	6.30	5
2200	0800	8	7.30	6
2300	0900	9	8.30	7
2400	1000	10	9.30	8

NEW ZEALAND TIME ZONE

UTC		
0000M	1200 N	12 N
0100	1300 PM	1 PM
0200	1400	2
0300	1500	3
0400	1600	4
0500	1700	5

0600	1800	6
0700	1900	7
0800	2000	8
0900	2100	9
1000	2200	10
1100	2300	11
1200N	2400 M	12 M
1300	0100 AM	1 AM
1400	0200	2
1500	0300	3
1600	0400	4
1700	0500	5
1800	0600	6
1900	0700	7
2000	0800	8
2100	0900	9
2200	1000	10
2300	1100	11
2400	1200 N	12 N

Table 5. Dimensions, Spacings and Lengths

TROPICAL BANDS

Band Metres	1 λ	2 ½λ	3 ¼λ	4 0.1λ	5 0.15λ	6 0.2λ	7 ¼λ	8 ¾λ	9 Refl.	10 Dir.
	ft.	ft.	ft.	ft.	ft.	ft.	ft.	ft.	ft.	ft.
49	164	82	41	16	25	33	39	118	82	73
60	197	98	49	20	30	40	47	142	98	89
75	246	123	62	25	37	49	59	178	123	113
90	298	149	75	30	45	60	71	215	149	132
120	410	205	103	41	62	82	98	296	205	180

MW BROADCAST BAND

Frequency MHz	1 λ	2 ½λ	3 ¼λ	4 0.1λ	5 0.15λ	6 0.2λ	7 ¼λ	8 ¾λ	9 Refl.	10 Dir.
1.5	656	328	164	65.6	97.1	131.2	156	473.3	328	300
1.0	984	492	246	98.4	145.6	196	234	710	492	450
0.6	1640	820	410	164	242.7	328	390	1183	820	750

Aerial Chart

A dimension chart such as that given in Table 5 provides quick answers in your design of a receiving aerial. Values are given for tropical bands and MW AM broadcast band. Except for highly directional aerials, lengths are relatively non-critical and little difference in performance is obtained when lengths depart as much as 15–20 per cent. However, for directional aerials using parasitic reflectors and directors, use a tollerance of no greater than about 3 per cent. Columns 1–3 give the free-space dimensions of a wavelength, half-wavelength and quarter-wavelength. Columns 4–6 are useful in spacing phased aerials and parasitic aerial elements. Columns 7 and 8 show the dimensions for each quarter-wave side of a dipole aerial and each three-quarter-wave side of a three-halves wavelength aerial. Columns 9 and 10 show lengths for parasitic reflectors and directors. Equations used to calculate the various dimensions are as follows:

λ Free Space	$=$	$984/f_{MHz}$
$\lambda/2$ Free Space	$=$	$492/f_{MHz}$
$\lambda/4$ Free Space	$=$	$246/f_{MHz}$
0.2λ Spacing	$=$	$196/f_{MHz}$
0.15λ Spacing	$=$	$145.6/f_{MHz}$
0.1λ Spacing	$=$	$98.4/f_{MHz}$
$\lambda/4$ Dipole	$=$	$234/f_{MHz}$
$3/4\lambda$ Dipole	$=$	$710/f_{MHz}$
Parasitic Reflector	$=$	$492/f_{MHz}$
Parasitic Director	$=$	$450/f_{MHz}$

SAFETY

The safety of an installation is your responsibility when erecting an aerial. The hazards are electrical shock, injury to a person or damage to property. Be thoughtful and wise. Do not erect an aerial where it can come in contact with electrical wires while you are making the installation or if it breaks loose from wind damage or fatigue after you have made the installation. Erect your aerial carefully so it cannot fall upon an individual or damage property during or after erection. As an extra safety precaution insulated wire is recommended.

1. QUARTER-WAVE AERIAL

A popular aerial for tropical-band reception is the simple quarter-wave long-wire of approximately 75-foot length, Fig.1(a). Length corresponds to approximately a quarter-wavelength on 90 metres. Good results are also obtained on the 49, 60 and 75 metre tropical bands. When a single-wire transmission line is used, its overall length makes a contribution and, therefore, acceptable results are obtained on the 120 metre band as well as segments of the medium-wave AM broadcast band.

Our preference is for an aerial wire of either 16 or 18 gauge SWG (14 or 16 gauge AWG) insulated wire. You need only bare the wire at places where connections or splices are made and where the end of the wire attaches to the receiver. Such wire provides a margin of safety and provides ease of erection and no noise problems when the aerial must be run through trees. Inexpensive quantities of wire can often be purchased at flea markets and surplus outlets. Of course, use a gauge that will take the mechanical mounting stress. The longer the aerial, the greater is the stress.

Results indicate that a combined vertical and horizontal construction such as that shown in Fig.1(b) is more favorable for multi-band reception. The 20-foot vertical segment improves results on the higher-frequency short-wave bands, while the overall length is favourable for the reception of the

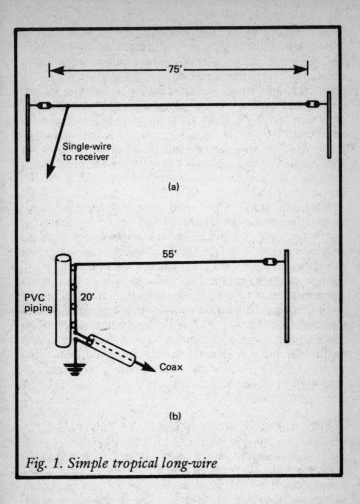

Fig. 1. Simple tropical long-wire

tropical bands. A coaxial line-feed system is used in conjunction with a 75-foot ground buried approximately 1 inch below the surface.

A tuner offers additional advantages for the avid listener such as easier identification, better results in the reception of weak signals, and minimization of the effects of fast-fade. A tuner is of help to the music-listening fan who prefers a solid signal. A tuner helps a receiver of limited sensitivity and/or one subject to image reception, and provides better results when a short aerial has to be used.

In general, when adjusting a tuner the capacitor(s) are first set to mid-scale. Then the inductor tap is moved to a setting of maximum signal. Now the variable capacitor(s) is tuned for peak performance. On occasion you can obtain a slightly better signal by bracketing the inductor. This means trying the inductor setting on each side of the previous one and retuning the capacitor(s). However, optimum results are usually obtained with the first procedure.

Here is a general tip in using a tuner with various aerial types. The broadcast bands occupy quite a spread of frequencies and, on occasion, the combination of aerial resistance and electrical length of transmission line accent line loss. Look into the matter if signal level on a particular band, when making comparison checks with another aerial, is much lower than seems sensible. A tuner helps in such a spot.

In using long-wire aerials inconsistent performance is often obtained from band-to-band. This can be the result of the changing impedance of the line at the point where it connects to the receiver input. Thus you can anticipate that a tuner may be very helpful on one band and result in no significant improvement on another.

2. DIPOLE AND QUARTER-WAVE VERTICALS

These two aerial types are basic. Often they are used for reference aerials for making comparisons with other styles. Usually the dipole is mounted horizontally and fed at the centre. As shown in Fig.2(a) each leg is one-quarter wavelength long, resulting in a half-wavelength aerial. The feedline can be 300 ohm line (TV transmission line) or 50–70 ohm coaxial line. For receiver application a good match is not a demanding consideration as it would be if the aerial were used for both transmit and receive.

A half-wavelength dipole is able to detect signals coming

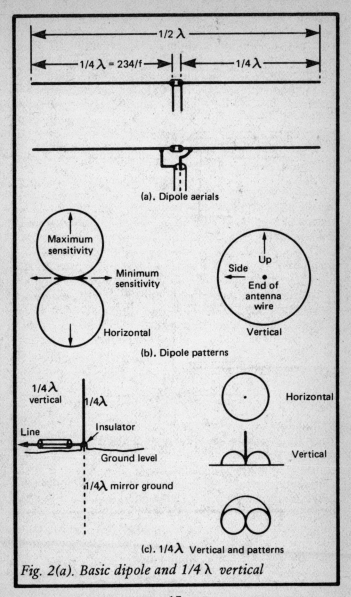

1/2 λ

1/4 λ = 234/f ← → 1/4 λ

(a). Dipole aerials

Maximum
sensitivity

Minimum
sensitivity

Horizontal

Up

Side

End of
antenna
wire

Vertical

(b). Dipole patterns

1/4 λ
vertical   1/4 λ

Line   Insulator

Ground level

1/4 λ mirror ground

Horizontal

Vertical

(c). 1/4 λ Vertical and patterns

Fig. 2(a). Basic dipole and 1/4 λ vertical

17

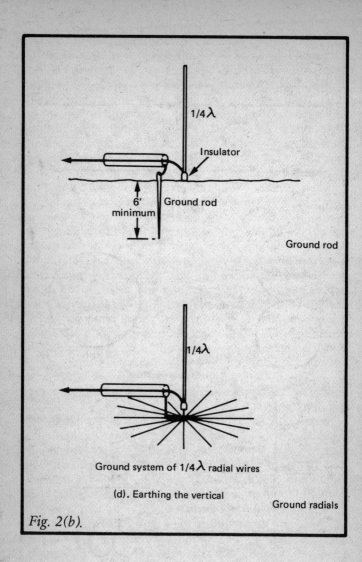

1/4λ

Insulator

6' minimum

Ground rod

Ground rod

1/4λ

Ground system of 1/4λ radial wires

(d). Earthing the vertical

Ground radials

Fig. 2(b).

18

in from all directions (all compass angles). However, it displays a maximum sensitivity to those signals that arrive perpendicular to, or broadside to the aerial wire as shown in Fig.2(b). This horizontal sensitivity pattern has a figure-eight appearance. Theoretically, it has little or no sensitivity parallel to the aerial wire. In practice the actual pattern fills in and departs from the theoretical so that the aerial does display a reasonable sensitivity in all directions. The lower the aerial is mounted, the greater is the departure from the theoretical figure-eight.

When elevated properly above earth and placed well away from obstructions the vertical sensitivity pattern is a circle as shown. This pattern too is theoretical because the earth and height of aerial above earth influence the vertical pattern.

The fundamental vertical aerial is a quarter-wavelength long as shown in Fig.2(c). The earth itself acts as a mirror quarter-wave segment. Earth conditions, in fact, have a great influence on the performance of a vertical aerial. The mirror segment of the quarter-wave vertical can be earth itself or a network of wires or conducting tubing that acts as a synthetic earth. If placed on the surface of the earth or a few inches below ground, such a low-resistance conducting surface can bring about a substantial improvement in aerial results.

The sensitivity patterns of a quarter-wave vertical are given in Fig.2(c). The horizontal sensitivity pattern is circular, indicating that the aerial accepts signals arriving from all compass directions. The vertical sensitivity pattern approximates a figure-eight slashed lengthwise. Note that the maximum sensitivity is concentrated at low vertical angles below $45°$. In fact, the net horizontal-vertical pattern is doughnut-like in appearance. In terms of DX reception, the low wave angle sensitivity is advantageous and can be obtained even though the aerial is mounted near earth level.

Two simple arrangements for a quarter-wave vertical are shown in Fig.2(d). A reasonable low-resistance link to earth is attained by driving a pipe (6 feet or longer) into the earth. Also an earth radial system comprised of three or more quarter-wave conductors buried about two inches beneath the surface helps to improve sensitivity at low vertical angles. If desired the two earthing methods can be combined.

The required length for the quarter-wave segment of a half-wavelength aerial or the length of a quarter-wave vertical can be obtained from Table 5. The theoretical value for the aerial resistance of a dipole is 72 ohms, while that of a quarter-wave vertical is 36 ohms. Again actual values depend upon height, ground conditions, and other factors. Nevertheless both aerials can be used to supply signals to coaxial or flat lines in a receiving only situation. In connecting a coaxial transmission line to a quarter-wave vertical, the inner conductor connects to the very bottom of the vertical aerial while the braid is connected to the pipe or other earthing system used.

In planning aerials for the tropical and MW broadcast bands, the full-length quarter-wave vertical is usually not feasible because of the height required. Often the practical aerial is part vertical and part horizontal, such as the long-wire plan of Fig.1(b). Thus the horizontal and vertical sensitivity patterns vary from band to band. There are too many variables involved.

Many of the aerials that follow are variations and/or elaborations of these fundamental types. The brief theoretical coverage of this section helps you better understand the basic concepts of aerials that follow.

3.   DIPOLE AND INVERTED DIPOLE

In tropical-band operation a dipole cut for a specific band performs very well and can be made to have some directional sensitivity to signals that arrive broadside to the wire direction. If there is one specific band you wish to favour it is a good choice. Mount it as high and clear as possible. Acceptable performance will also be obtained on the other tropical bands.

In erecting a dipole recall that the overall length of the aerial is twice the quarter-wave dimension given in Table 5. On the 49 metre band the overall length is not great, approaching 80 feet as shown in Fig.3(a). Dipole overall length increases in significant steps for each new lower-frequency tropical band. You must measure your available space for aerial erection.

The inverted dipole of Fig.3(b) does save some space and

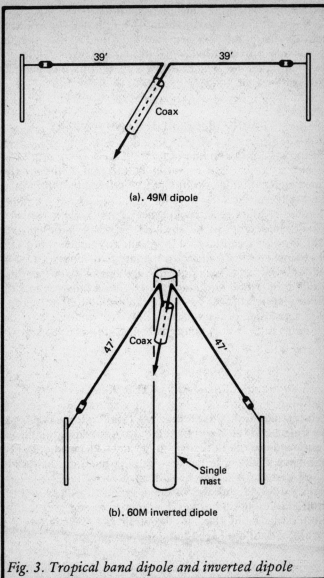

(a). 49M dipole

(b). 60M inverted dipole

Fig. 3. Tropical band dipole and inverted dipole

requires only a single mounting mast. The far end of each segment can be close to earth. The diagonal slope of each element means that the overall space required is less than if the aerial was a straight horizontal dipole. The inverted dipole is a good performer and the two aerial segments also augment the mast guying.

4. INVERTED DIPOLE AND JUMPERS

In as much as the far end of each aerial element is near earth, jumpers can be used conveniently to resonate the inverted dipole on more than one frequency. Refer to the arrangement of Fig.4.

The length of each aerial segment between the transmission line connection point and the insulator/jumper corresponds to the resonant length needed for 49 metre operation. When the two jumpers are disconnected the inverted dipole is set for 49 metre band operation. When the two jumpers are connected additional aerial wire is added. In the example shown the added length has been cut for operation on the 60 metre band.

In changing bands you need only free one side at a time from its earth-level holding position and make the appropriate jumpers changeover.

5. CROSS-INVERTED DIPOLES

The arrangement of Fig.5 does not require the use of jumpers to obtain two-band resonance. If space is available, two dipoles can be connected to the feed point and then mounted to four tie-down points such that the dipole elements are 90° related as shown in Fig.5. The dimensions given in Fig.5 have been selected for the 60 and 90 metre bands. In fact, space available, the combination provides good operation over the five tropical bands. It also provides acceptable results on the AM MW broadcast band as well.

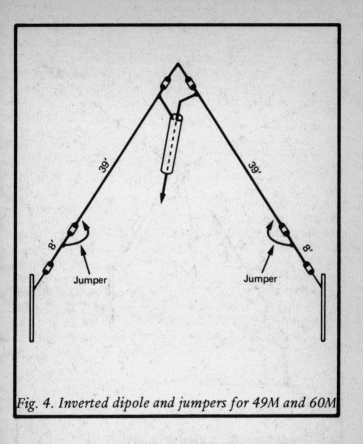

Fig. 4. *Inverted dipole and jumpers for 49M and 60M*

6.   UNLIKE-SEGMENT DIPOLES

The dipole of Fig.6 has segments of unequal length and provides acceptable performance in a much smaller mounting
area. In this example one-half of the dipole is out to the 60
metre band; the other half, the 90 metre band. This aerial does
very well considering the little space required. In our checks
the same idea can be adapted to the inverted dipole and
jumper combination of Fig.4. Instead of using jumpers simply
cut one segment for 49 metres the other for 60.

23

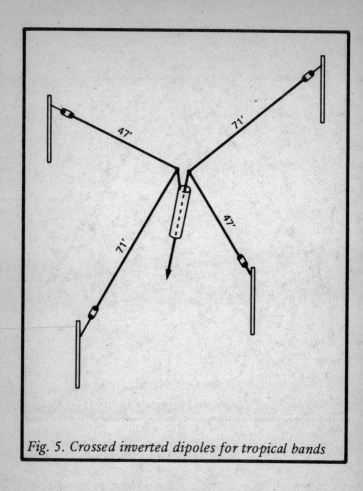

Fig. 5. Crossed inverted dipoles for tropical bands

7. LONG-WIRE VERTICAL HELIX

If you have a confined mounting space try a vertical. A very low-cost and effective vertical can be constructed for the tropical bands using insulated hook-up wire and PVC (poly-vinyl chloride) piping. PVC piping is light-weight and is a good high-frequency insulator. Two 10-foot sections and one 4-foot

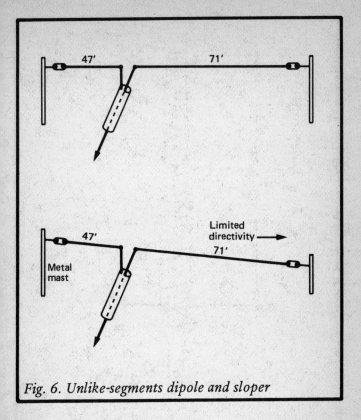

Fig. 6. Unlike-segments dipole and sloper

section of telescoping PVC piping can be bolted together into an easy-lift mast, Fig.7. After a metal fence post has been driven into the earth, the completed mast can be slipped over the post, providing a firm mounting. The aerial is practically self-supporting, although you may wish to use two rope guys to hold it precisely vertical. The inner diameter of the three sections were 2, 1½ and 1 inch. The middle section was telescoped two feet into the lower section and bolted. Likewise the short top section was inserted two feet into the middle section and bolted. A through resting bolt was positioned two feet from the bottom of the lower section. When slipped over

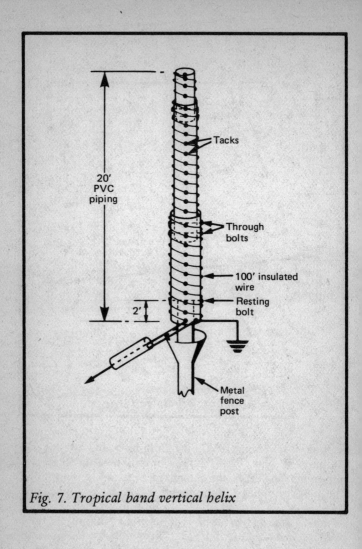

Fig. 7. Tropical band vertical helix

the metal fence post this bolt will rest over its top.

The helical aerial was constructed using a 100-foot spool of vinyl-covered 20 gauge SWG (18 gauge AWG) wire. It was

26

wound in helical fashion around the mast supported by spaced tacks hammered into the PVC piping. Tack spacing along the bottom section was 3 inches and then spacing was diminished to 2 inches and 1½ inches over the top two sections in such a manner that the full 100-foot length could be accommodated on the 20-foot mast. At the very bottom of the mast two terminal bolt/nut pairs were mounted. The helical wire along with the inner conductor of the coaxial transmission line were connected to one terminal, while the braid and an earth were connected to the second terminal. If you have a good receiver earth connect no external earth at the base of the mast. An external earth could be made to the metal fence post or a radial wire connected to the earth terminal if your receiver earth is poor. Do not use two earths.

The aerial does very well considering the limited space required. Tropical-band performance was quite comparable to considerably longer horizontal aerials. Good results were also obtained on the 25, 31 and 41 metre bands. There were acceptable results on the higher-frequency bands from 11 to 22 metres.

Additional detail on using PVC masts for aerial construction can be found in book number BP132: *25 Simple Short-Wave Broadcast Band Aerials*, by the same author and publishers as this book.

8.   TROPICAL AND MW BAND LONG-WIRE

Two plans for a 100-foot long-wire aerial are given in Fig.8. Comparisons were made between the vertical and horizontal aerials of Fig.7 and 8. 20-foot PVC masts were used in the construction of the horizontal aerials. Such masts can be used in the construction of the various aerial types that follow. Metal or wood masts can be used if you prefer.

In example (a) the overall length of the aerial is 100 feet. An approximate 18-foot segment of the overall length is mounted vertically along the mast, dropping down to terminals to which the coaxial line to the receiver is attached. If you prefer you can use a single wire feeder to the receiver.

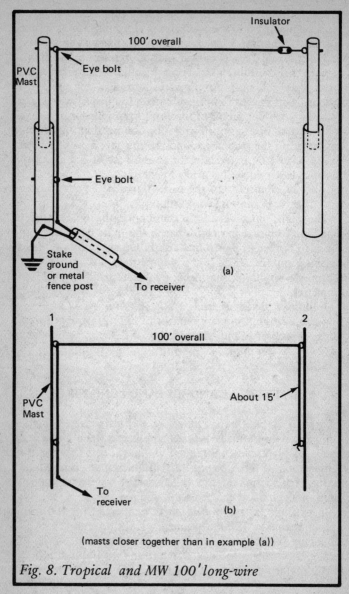

Fig. 8. Tropical and MW 100' long-wire

If you use coaxial line, earth its braid well at only one end, receiver or aerial. Screw eye or eyebolts hold the vertical segment of the aerial in position.

Performance of example (a) aerial as compared to the vertical helix of Fig.7 was quite similar. There was some additional signal level on the lower-frequency tropical bands. But if you were also a medium-wave broadcast band listener there was a pronounced increase in received signal level as compared to the vertical aerial of Fig.7. However, the aerial does require additional mounting space. If required, the required space can be cut down using the arrangement of Fig.8(b). Note that the two masts are nearer to each other and the far end of the aerial drops down about 15 feet along the mast. The aerial end is looped around the bottom eyebolt and tightened. Each mast consisted of two 10-foot telescoping sections of PVC piping. As in Fig.7, the masts were lifted and slipped over metal fence posts. Consequently the total mast height was at least 20 feet.

9. 3/2 WAVELENGTH ON 60 METRES

Space available, some added sensitivity on the tropical bands and a decided increase in received level on the MW band can be obtained by using a 3/4 wavelength aerial, Fig.9. Each 3/4 wavelength segment must have a length of 142 feet when cut for the 60 metre band. Refer to the 3/4 wavelength dimensions in Table 5. Note that this length also corresponds approximately to the recommended quarter-wavelength dipole dimension for a frequency of 1.5 MHz on the MW AM broadcast band. Mount the aerial line as high and clear as possible. Coaxial or flat transmission line can be used. The inverted dipole configuration performs very well, saves some space and requires but a single mast. Often a single high mast is more affordable than two lower masts. In free-space the sensitivity pattern is a six-lobe affair. However, at normal mounting heights such an aerial is essentially non-directional.

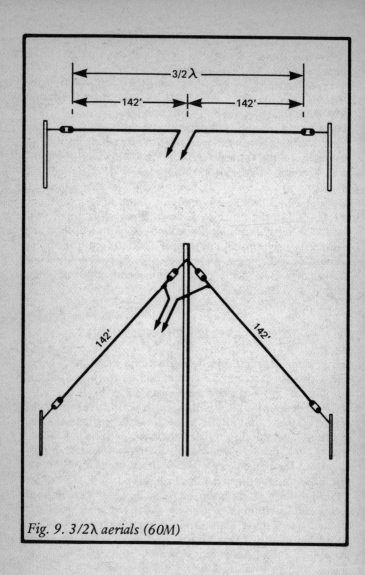

Fig. 9. 3/2λ aerials (60M)

10. VEE BEAM

A long 3/2 wavelength aerial can be made to have some reasonable directivity by tilting its two segments forward as shown in Fig.10. The acute angle between the two-element segments should be about 105–120 degrees. In many parts of the world considerable time is spent listening for the Central and South American broadcast stations. The short vee beam can be positioned to favour this direction from your location and, at the same time, acceptable omnidirectional performance is obtained.

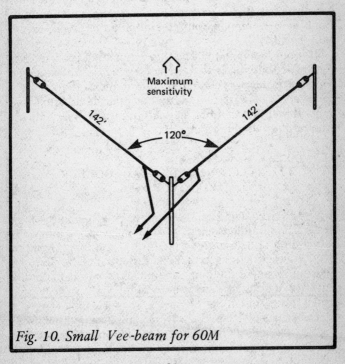

Fig. 10. Small Vee-beam for 60M

11.   MW VERTICAL LADDER

A quarter-wavelength on 1 MHz (approximate centre of MW AM broadcast band) is approximately 234 feet. Refer to Chart 5. If mounting space is a problem the aerial wire can be strung in ladder fashion to obtain proper overall length. The aerial of Fig.11 uses two PVC piping masts separated by approximately 40 feet. The aerial wire is run through eyebolts attached to the PVC mast. There are five ladder steps. Consequently total length of wire would be 200 feet (50 × 40). However, the aerial wire also runs down the mast and by adding this figure to the total, as well as the length of the aerial wire leading to the receiver it is no problem to set up a quarter-wavelength aerial of 234 feet and more.

Good MW band performance is obtained. Additionally, acceptable results are obtained on the tropical and short-wave bands as well, varying band to band as a function of overall aerial length.

If a single-wire feed line is used employ a good receiver earth. If coaxial line is used establish a good earth at either the aerial or the receiver but *not* at both locations. If you have a good earth at the receiver and an other-than-ideal earth at the aerial it will detract from the performance of this and most tropical and long-wire aerials.

12.   CLOSED HORIZONTAL LOOP FOR
TROPICAL BANDS

A loop-aerial configuration is a space-saver and provides good performance on the tropical bands. Overall length corresponds to a full wavelength on the band for which it is cut. Refer to the 1-wavelength column of Table 5. Separation between the masts or mounting positions corresponds to one quarter of the full-wave dimension. Such an aerial provides a reasonable match to a coaxial or flat TV line.

The example of Fig.12 is cut for the 60 metre band. Note that the overall length of wire is approximately 200 feet. The aerial provides good performance on the band to which it is

Fig. 11. MW vertical ladder

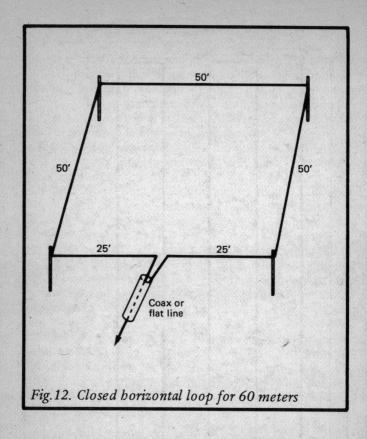

Fig.12. Closed horizontal loop for 60 meters

cut and the two adjacent bands. Acceptable performance is obtained on all of the tropical bands. The loop-aerial configuration need not be high and good results are obtained using 10 foot of PVC piping or two telescoped 10-foot sections for each mast. The latter plan will elevate the top of the aerial approximately 18 feet from earth.

13. OPEN HORIZONTAL-LOOP CONFIGURATIONS

All-band performance even up into the AM MW band can be obtained using the open-loop configuration of Fig.13. The aerial functions as a tropical long-wire. Consequently overall wire length is a quarter wavelength up into the MW broadcast band. A single wire feed is used.

Example (a) has the same dimensions as the closed loop of Fig.12. The overall length of wire is approximately 200 feet which corresponds to a quarter wavelength up into the MW band. In the tropical bands it functions as a longer electrical long-wire. Performance is not peaked on any one band but good average performance is obtained.

You may wish to combine aerials 12 and 13. Use a coaxial or flat line. For closed-loop operation both wires of the transmission line are connected as in Fig.12. For open-loop operation just connect one conductor (centre conductor of coaxial line) and leave the other line or coaxial braid disconnected. Drop the two ends of the aerial wire down near earth level to provide easy access to making the aerial change-over.

In setting up a tropical or MW aerial take advantage of whatever size lot is available. Aerial can be two-sided or three-sided as shown in Fig.13(b). Select the combination that will give you the greatest overall length according to the arrangement of your erection site.

14. DOUBLE OPEN-LOOP FOR TROPICAL AND MW BANDS

If you are really cramped for space it is still possible to obtain a full quarter-wavelength dimension on the MW band. The arrangement of Fig.14 shows a good performing combination despite the confined mounting area. Spacing between masts is 30 feet and the overall length of the aerial wire is approximately 210 feet; a length that is a quarter wavelength well up into the MW broadcast band.

If you are only interested in tropical band operations, you

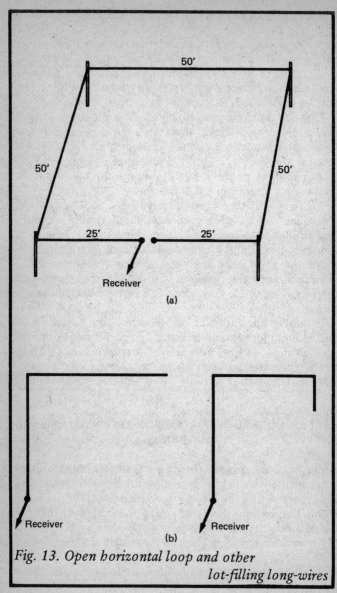

Fig. 13. Open horizontal loop and other
lot-filling long-wires

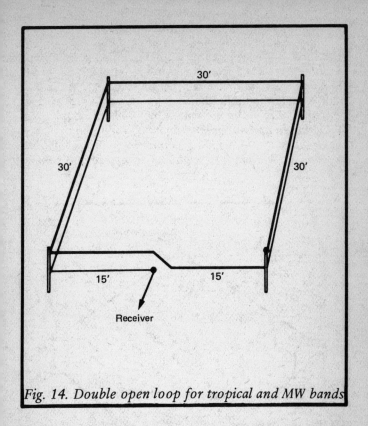

Fig. 14. Double open loop for tropical and MW bands

can cut back the side length from 30 to 15 feet. In this case the overall length will correspond to a quarter wavelength on the 120 metre band. Configuration need not be squared and it can be triangular or rectangular if that meets your space requirements better. Use your available space to best advantage in obtaining the desired overall long-wire length.

15.   LITTLE SQUARED RHOMBIC

The small rhombic-shaped aerial of Fig.15 is a good all-band performer. It can be erected in an area less than 65 feet square. The four sides are of the same length and all angles are $90°$; it is a perfect square. Rhombic can be supported by four telescoped PVC piping sections or by metal or wooden masts. Transmission line is connected to one corner of the aerial. The aerial wires at the opposite corner can either be shorted together or left open depending upon operating conditions

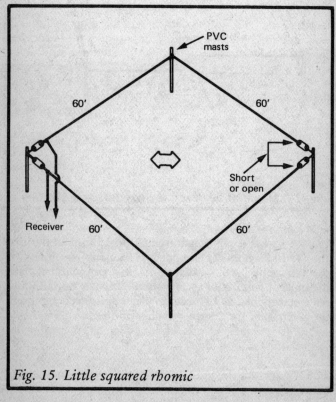

Fig. 15. Little squared rhomic

you prefer. A simple halyard arrangement can be used at this mast to permit the aerial to be raised and lowered to remove or attach the shorting jumper.

A rhombic is basically bi-directional in the two directions indicated by the double arrow in Fig.15. A short low rhombic of this type has some directivity but not so sharp as to curtail good omnidirectional performance. You can favour signals a small amount by erecting the rhombic so that the diagonal line between feedpoint and diagonally opposite mast faces the planned direction. The directivity is most pronounced for the aerial of Fig.15 on 60 metres and for several of the higher-frequency short-wave bands, from 11 to 25 metres. Leg length from feedpoint to opposite corner approximates a 3/4 wave-length on the 49/60 metre bands. In general, better performance on the lower-frequency tropical bands was obtained with the far end shorted. General performance on the high-frequency short-wave bands was obtained with the far end open. On the 49 metre band performance was about the same with either connection.

16.   MULTIPLE AERIAL ARRAY

The special aerial construction of Fig.16 combines the features of types given in Figs. 13, 14 and 15. PVC piping was used and masts were spaced exactly the same as the installation of Fig.15. Separations were again 60 feet. However, aerial wires are brought down to a low access level by feeding them down through screw eyes for masts 1 and 3. In the case of 3 note that it is possible to short or not-short the far end of a rhombic. The mast associated with the feedpoint has three terminals. Connections as shown are for rhombic operation. Note that the inner conductor of the coaxial line connects to terminal 2 and the braid to terminal 1. The two terminals of mast 3 can be either operated open or closed for the rhombic configuration.

The previous connections permit you to favour either tropical or short-wave bands operation. The aerial array can also be operated as an open-loop. This manner of connection

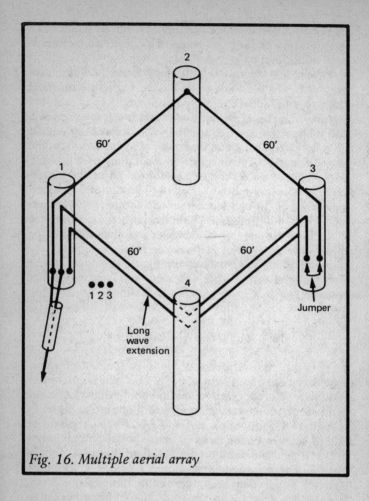

Fig. 16. Multiple aerial array

will set up a good combination for operation on the tropical and medium-wave bands. This mode of operation is obtained by disconnecting the braid of the coaxial line from terminal 1. Thus single-line feed is obtained using the inner conductor of the coaxial line. If you prefer a separate single wire lead can be substituted for the coaxial line. This single lead should be connected to terminal 2. The jumper short should be closed at mast 3. If you now follow the aerial wire from terminal 2 you will notice that it makes a complete loop ending at terminal 1. No connection is made at terminal 1. This manner of connection performs well over the entire medium wave broadcast band (540 – 1600 kHz) but favours the low-frequency half of the band. If you wish to favour high-frequency end of the MW band you can remove the jumper at mast 3.

A final mode of operation can be set up to favour the long-wave (LW band) by adding an additional 140 feet of aerial wire. Note that there is a length of aerial wire from terminal 3 of mast 1 that extends from mast 1 over a path to mast 4 and then on to mast 3 where it is terminated. This additional length of line can be added by connecting a jumper between terminals 1 and 3 of mast 1. Also the jumper must be connected between the two terminals associated with mast 3.

In conclusion, the versatile arrangement of Fig.16 provides a selective choice of listening activities using a good performing receiver. You may wish to do some additional aerial experimentation using the conveniences of this plan.

17.   SPACE-SAVING DIPOLE

Another technique that can be used to squeeze a full-length tropical dipole on a small plot is shown in Fig.17. As noted in Table 5, dipole lengths vary from 47 feet to 98 feet on the tropical bands. Stretched out, a dipole would require a bit more than twice these figures. A simple inverted dipole results in some space saving. However, the use of two masts as shown in Fig.17 can result in additional space squeezing. In example (a) the dipole is stretched out horizontally; in example (b) the outer segment of each quarter-wave element can be bent at a 90° to 150° angle depending upon plot accommodations. The higher the mast, the less is the required linear space. Bending the element ends away from the straight line can be useful in permitting a full-length dipole in an even smaller available space. For this aerial structure use as high a mast as possible and stretch out the aerial elements as far as you can. ·

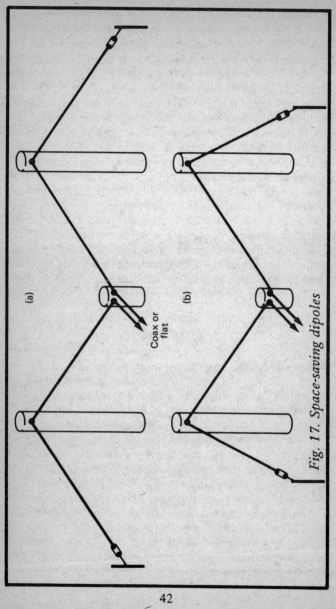

Coax or
flat

(a)

(b)

Fig. 17. Space-saving dipoles

A dipole installed for the 90 metre band requires two 71-foot elements and an overall length near 250 feet if the aerial is stretched out in a straight line horizontally. However, if you sawtooth and deviate from the linear it can be accommodated in a substantially smaller space, producing compromise results that are quite satisfactory as compared to a too-short aerial wire.

18. INDOOR TROPICAL LONG-WIRE

Don't push tropical band listening aside if you are not able to erect an outside aerial. A random length of wire can do wonders indoors, Fig.18. Use flexible insulated wire of 20 gauge SWG (18 gauge AWG) or thinner. A 60–70-foot length laid along the sides of a small room, even though it is doubled back upon itself does well. It can be run under the carpet and/or taped to the floor along the outer perimeter of the room. If you can stretch out the full length in a reasonably straight line by extension into the next room or along a hall you can make a definite improvement in the reception of the lower-frequency tropical bands and medium-wave broadcast bands.

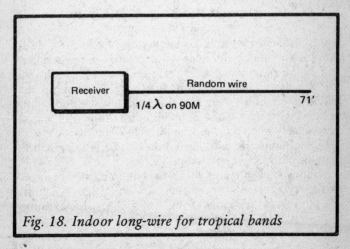

Fig. 18. Indoor long-wire for tropical bands

Band-by-band reception is often inconsistent. A shift of position can often improve reception on some bands. At the same time it may cut down signal levels on another band. A little experimentation helps if you wish to seek an average performance.

Be certain to use an effective earth for the reception of these low-frequency signals. A cold water pipe or attachment does very well. Stay away from connections to electrical wires and appliances. A surge of voltage can damage a modern solid-state receiver. A tuner can be of tremendous help when you are receiving tropical band signals with a short aerial. If you are an avid fan don't be dismayed by the additional controls. Make a log of optimum tuner settings for the various bands so you can reset quickly when switching bands.

In a dwelling with metal beams and/or metallic siding there can be a shielding effect. In this case try to route your random long-wire near windows. Perhaps you can get part of the long-wire outdoors at windows or, perhaps, a porch ceiling. Take care not to encroach upon your neighbour's property and route it so it cannot come it contact with electrical wires or cause damage if it becomes loose or falls.

19.   INDOOR TROPICAL OPEN LOOPS

Better performance can be obtained with a higher aerial. In as much as appearance is not always an overwhelming consideration in the radio room, a long-wire aerial with a total length that depends upon room size can be strung completely around the periphery of the room near the ceiling and, then down one wall to the receiver as shown in example (a). Installed around a reasonably large room a long-wire close to 70 feet is very possible. Results can hold many surprises. Be certain, though, that you have a good earth on the receiver.

As mentioned previously there are quite a number of inconsistencies in the performance of an indoor aerial. Sometimes you are able to take advantage of these variables. For example, in the installation of an indoor open loop you may wish to take advantage of the switching arrangement given in example

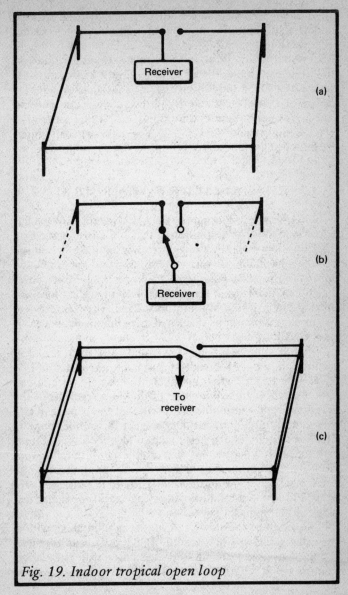

Fig. 19. Indoor tropical open loop

(b). You will find that the performance band-by-band can vary considerably depending upon what lead you switch to the receiver input.

If your room is small and your aim is good reception on low-frequency tropical bands or even the MW broadcast band, the use of a double-loop configuration as shown in example (c) can be of help. Total aerial length could well correspond to an approximate quarter-wavelength on 120 metres. To improve performance you may wish to use a switchable input for this open double-loop.

20. MW QUARTER-WAVE AERIALS

A quarter-wavelength aerial on the AM MW broadcast band is a long one. Nevertheless an aerial that is a quarter-wave long displays a low impedance to the receiver and takes advantage of the maximum signal current delivered at this low impedance. Cutting your aerial to proper length can deliver 2 to 10 dB more signal than a short aerial or one cut for some other position in the MW broadcast band. The quarter-wavelength dimension can be calculated using the standard quarter-wave equation (length in feet = 234/frequency in megahertz).

Physical dimensions for low-, mid- and high-frequency sections of the AM broadcast band are given in Table 5. Typical lengths are given in Fig.20. In example (a) you can choose a length to favour either of the three segments of the broadcast band. Favouring one portion of the band may give you 2 to 6 dB more signal than one cut for another portion. This can be significant when trying to identify a weak broadcast signal. If you are not that avid a fan, a quarter-wave calculated for the mid-band will provide good compromise performance over the entire band. These long aerials can also be used for tropical band reception. They have some directivity off the ends on these frequencies.

Two or three individual aerials can be used along with a switching arrangement to choose the proper band segment. However, there is some interaction among aerials. The plan of example (b) is attractive. In the erection of the aerial make it

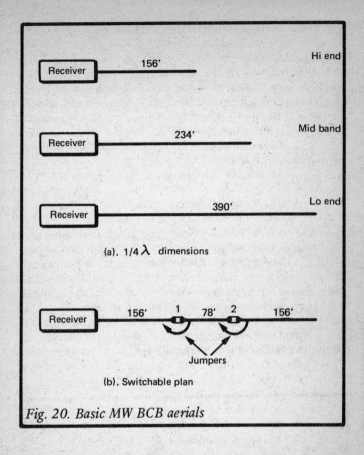

(a). 1/4 λ dimensions

(b). Switchable plan

Fig. 20. Basic MW BCB aerials

easy to lower or drop connections down two of the individual support masts to permit a jumper arrangement to be used in shifting band sections. Both jumpers open permits operation at the high end. Jumper 1 closed tunes the aerial for the mid-band. Low-end operation is obtained when both jumpers are closed.

21. MW AND LW LONG-WIRE

A 600-foot long-wire is an attractive length for an aerial to be used for medium-wave and long-wave reception, Fig.21. The 600-foot length acts as a quarter-wavelength on 390 kHz (frequency in megahertz = 234/600). This same length of wire acts as a three-quarter wavelength aerial at approximately the centre of the MW broadcast band. A 3/4 wavelength aerial also displays a minimum impedance to the receiver and, therefore, a maximum signal current.

Such an aerial is also useful on the tropical bands as well as on the short-wave bands where it displays a significant end-directivity. Performance changes from band to band as a function of the end impedance at the band frequency. An aerial of this type lower to the ground displays a more omni-directional pattern and less directivity off the ends.

A very low-mounting height, say 5 foot, displays good directivity but with less signal sensitivity. However, the aerial does display beverage-type characteristics on the tropical bands. A beverage aerial is noted for its extremely low sensitivity broadside to the direction of the wire. Consequently both tropical and MW band operation with this low mounting can be used to favour a signal arriving from a preferred direction at the same time it reduces signal levels arriving broadside to the wire direction.

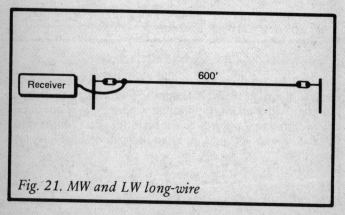

Fig. 21. MW and LW long-wire

48

22. THE BASIC BEVERAGE

The beverage aerial is used extensively for MW broadcast band DXing. The aerial wire is stretched out in the direction you wish to receive. Mounted low to the earth the aerial will reject signals that arrive broadside to the aerial wire. Strong interfering signals can be cut way down in level and a far-away station made to dominate if the aerial can be oriented in that direction. A typical height above ground is 5 feet and minimum overall length should be 1000 feet or more. However, some significant directivity and broadside rejection can be accomplished for even a shorter length.

As the aerial is raised above ground, there is a gradual changeover from the beverage characteristics to that of a long-wire aerial. Signal pick-up in the favoured direction even increases. However, results indicate that the side pick-up increases at a higher rate. Consequently there is not as much suppression of the side pick-up of strong signals.

A beverage aerial can be terminated to a good earth through a non-conductive resistance of several hundred ohms. By so doing the aerial is more uni-directional in a direction from the receiver and towards the termination. There is no additional signal pick-up but there is rejection of signals coming from the back.

Experimentation with the termination ohmic value as well

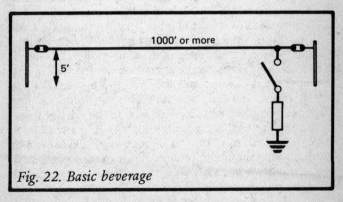

Fig. 22. Basic beverage

as the use of more than one beverage in a phasing arrangement are used by some of the more avid broadcast-band DXers. Space requirements and complexities take this type of array out of the simple aerial classification.

23. LONG-WIRE/BEVERAGE ARRAY

PVC piping can be used to advantage in the construction of long-wire and beverage arrays as shown in Fig.23. A long-wire aerial of a specific length can be run along the top of PVC piping masts. These can be spaced approximately 60 feet apart and the aerial extended out as far as you wish. Aerial wires can be run through the eyebolts, making it easy to change over between a beverage or a long-wire simply by providing a convenient way of detaching the wire at one end and rolling it up on a spool. Of course, the two aerials can be operated jointly. There is interaction on some frequencies.

The beverage aerial can be run along the mast at a low point that is no more than 5 foot above earth.

24. MW ATTIC LADDER

An attic often provides adequate space for erection of a very long aerial that will improve performance on the MW broadcast band as well as tropical bands. Results do vary band to band but, if you are a critical listener, they can be peaked with the use of a tuner. MW broadcast reception is excellent.

Such an aerial is wound in orderly fashion among the studs and beams of the attic, Fig.24. Our own installation was wound back and forth along both sloping sides of the attic ceiling. A continuous piece of hook-up wire was used. An optimum dimension of a quarter-wavelength between 0.9 and 1 MHz (about 240 feet) was used. This length included the length of the down lead from the attic to the receiver input. It is surprising how conveniently this very long aerial can be fitted into a rather small attic or roof space. Layout can be square or rectangular and accommodated to the configuration of the mounting site. Stretch it out as far as you can before using the doubling back of the ladder arrangement.

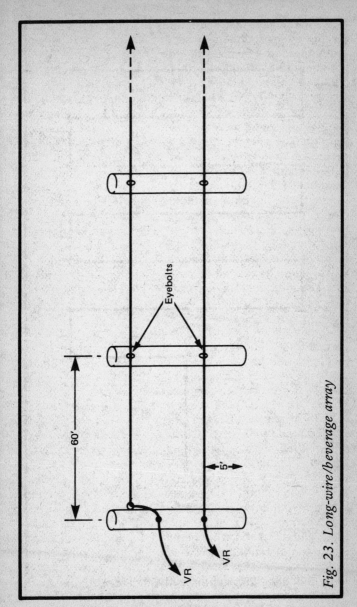

Fig. 23. Long-wire/beverage array

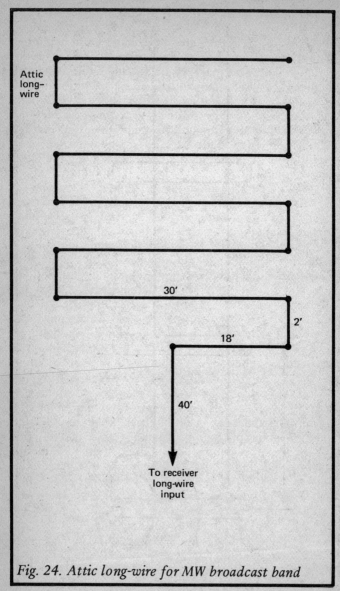

Attic long-wire

30'

2'

18'

40'

To receiver long-wire input

Fig. 24. Attic long-wire for MW broadcast band

25. ACTIVE AERIALS

The active aerial incorporates a very short aerial and a pre-amplifier that comes ahead of the aerial input of your receiver, Fig.25. The amplifier is a low-noise unit and is able to build up the weak received signal to a level acceptable to the receiver input. Such a system is especially attractive for older receivers and those with limited sensitivity and signal-to-noise ratio. Improvement is often marginal for a modern top-line receiver. However, even with a top-line receiver improvement is often significant in the reception of weak tropical and MW band signals.

The two active types are shown in Fig.25. In example (a) the active aerial is a single unit affair including a very short aerial and the amplifier/control facility. Output is connected to receiver input with a short length of coaxial cable. This type does quite well in improving reception on limited-performance receivers.

A more versatile and better-performing active aerial is the type that separates the aerial and the amplifier from the controls as shown in example (b). Fine results are obtained with this type of unit even if you use a top-line, high-performance receiver. Only a top-performing outdoor aerial will do better in the reception of tropical and MW signals. The advantages of the "separates" idea is that the aerial itself is somewhat longer and the aerial can be mounted high and clear.

The unit used was a MFJ/1024* mounted at the top of a short length of PVC piping and clamped to the vent pipe of the house. Appropriate length of coaxial cable connects the pre-amplifier to the control unit that sits beside the receiver.

Even the apartment or condominium dweller can derive much from this type of installation because the unit can be attached to a window, porch roof or railing. Such an installation provides some clearance from shielding effects by the metallic surfaces associated with buildings.

---

*MJF Enterprises, PO Box 494, Mississippi State, MS, 39762, U .S.A.

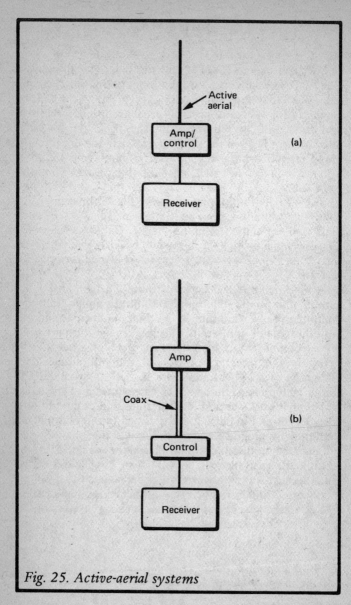

Fig. 25. Active-aerial systems

Please note following is a list of other titles that are available in our range of Radio, Electronics and Computer Books.

These should be available from all good Booksellers, Radio Component Dealers and Mail Order Companies.

However, should you experience difficulty in obtaining any title in your area, then please write directly to the publisher enclosing payment to cover the cost of the book plus adequate postage.

If you would like a complete catalogue of our entire range of Radio, Electronics and Computer Books then please send a Stamped Addressed Envelope to:

BERNARD BABANI (publishing) LTD
THE GRAMPIANS
SHEPHERDS BUSH ROAD
LONDON W6 7NF
ENGLAND